In the beginning God created the heavens and the earth.

If you would like to read the whole of this story,
you will find it on pages 3-4 of your Child's Bible.

1

God said: "Let us make man in our own image and likeness. I will give him the animals and plants. I will entrust them all to him." And God gave his creatures Paradise.

If you would like to read the whole of this story,
you will find it on pages 4-5 of your Child's Bible.

The man and the woman lived in the garden that God had entrusted to them. They lived in harmony with the animals. They were blessed, for God was their friend.

If you would like to read the whole of this story, you will find it on pages 6-7 of your Child's Bible.

Noah and his family had always loved God. One day, a great flood of water came over the earth, and God said: "Because you have always loved me, I will now faithfully protect you and look after you!"

If you would like to read the whole of this story,
you will find it on pages 9-10 of your Child's Bible.

Abraham called out to God: "I trust in you!" And God saw Abraham's Faith. So it was that Abraham, although he was very old, was granted the child which he had wanted for so long. And he came to understand that for God nothing is impossible!

If you would like to read the whole of this story,
you will find it on pages 11-12 of your Child's Bible.

Sara and Abraham gave their son the name which God
himself had chosen: Isaac.

If you would like to read the whole of this story,
you will find it on pages 13-14 of your Child's Bible.

Isaac blessed his son Jacob: "May God give you everything you need on Earth."

If you would like to read the whole of this story,
you will find it on pages 14-16 of your Child's Bible.

Jacob loved Joseph more than his other sons. Because of this, the others became jealous. One day they seized their brother Joseph and threw him down a well. Then they sold him for 20 silver pieces to a foreign merchant. And so Joseph went to Egypt with the merchant.

If you would like to read the whole of this story,
you will find it on pages 16-19 of your Child's Bible.

The daughter of the Egyptian Pharaoh saw the baby Moses floating in a basket on the river. She said: "I feel sorry for you! I want to save you!" She had the basket brought to the shore and the baby looked after. So Moses was rescued by the Pharaoh's daughter.

If you would like to read the whole of this story,
you will find it on pages 20-21 of your Child's Bible.

God spoke to Moses from a burning thorn bush. He told Moses his name: "I am who I am." That means that God is always there for us, for all time – including today!

If you would like to read the whole of this story,
you will find it on pages 21-22 of your Child's Bible.

God said to Moses: "This very night, Pharaoh will let you go. Be ready to leave." The people of Israel never forgot this first Passover night. Each year they celebrate Passover, the feast of the Exodus, and tell their children: with his mighty hand, God freed us from slavery under the Egyptians.

If you would like to read the whole of this story, you will find it on pages 24-25 of your Child's Bible.

God said to Moses: "Stretch out your hand over the sea so that my people can pass through." Moses obeyed. Immediately the sea divided into two, and so the people of Israel walked to safety on dry land. They sang: "Praise be to God, praise him, for he is strong and mighty!"

If you would like to read the whole of this story, you will find it on pages 25-26 of your Child's Bible.

On the top of Mount Sinai, God gave Moses the Ten Commandments. They are true for all people and for all times. Moses wrote them down on two stone tablets.

If you would like to read the whole of this story,
you will find it on pages 28-29 of your Child's Bible.

For 40 years, God's people were in the wilderness. Meanwhile Moses was growing old. He climbed to the summit of Mount Nebo. There, God showed him the whole of the land which he had promised to his people. Then Moses died and the Israelites mourned him for 30 days.

If you would like to read the whole of this story,
you will find it on page 30 of your Child's Bible.

David was a shepherd boy. He trusted in God and God was with him. That is why David was so brave and joyful. He sang and played many songs of praise in God's honour. Later he became king of the People of God.

If you would like to read the whole of this story,
you will find it on pages 34-37 of your Child's Bible.

King Solomon built a house for God. He prayed a great deal:
"O Lord, our God, hear our prayers and our praise!"

If you would like to read the whole of this story,
you will find it on pages 37-38 of your Child's Bible.

There was a great drought on the earth. The people were in
great distress. The prophet Elijah prayed to God – and very
soon the saving rain began to fall.

If you would like to read the whole of this story,
you will find it on pages 42-43 of your Child's Bible.

God's exiled people had to stay in Babylon for about 40 years. Then the Persian king Cyrus conquered Babylon. He said: "Everyone who belongs to God's people will be allowed to go back to Jerusalem." At this, God's people rejoiced that they could return home.

If you would like to read the whole of this story,
you will find it on page 48 of your Child's Bible.

For three days Jonah was in the belly of the whale. Then it spat him out, safe and sound, onto the sea shore. Then God said to him: "Go to Niniveh, that great city. Proclaim to them everything I tell you to say."

If you would like to read the whole of this story,
you will find it on pages 53-54 of your Child's Bible.

God sent the Archangel Gabriel as his messenger to the
Virgin Mary. He announced to her: "God has chosen you to
be the Mother of the Messiah. Your Child will be called
Jesus, the Redeemer of all mankind!"

If you would like to read the whole of this story,
you will find it on pages 57-58 of your Child's Bible.

In a poor and humble stable Jesus is born into our world. A great throng of angels gather round him and sing: "Glory to God in the highest! For he is the Lord!"

If you would like to read the whole of this story,
you will find it on page 59 of your Child's Bible.

In the temple, the teachers of the Holy Scriptures are amazed at the boy, Jesus. He is only 12 years old, and yet he speaks with great wisdom – for he is the Son of God.

If you would like to read the whole of this story,
you will find it on pages 62-63 of your Child's Bible.

Jesus asks John to baptise him. Then the skies open and God the Father speaks from Heaven: "You are my beloved Son; I am very pleased with you."

If you would like to read the whole of this story,
you will find it on page 64 of your Child's Bible.

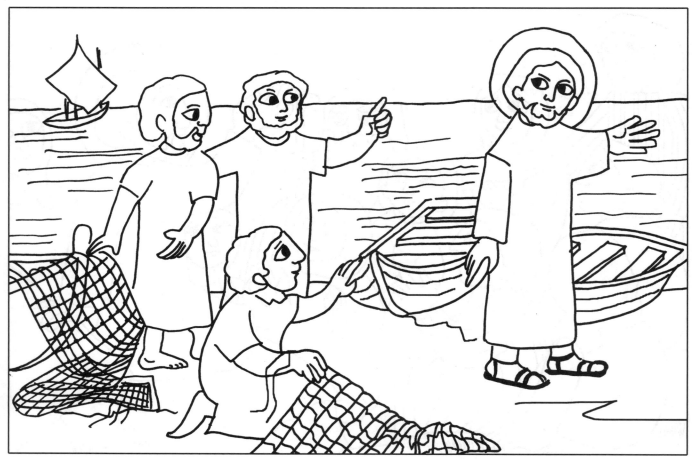

On the shore of the Sea of Galilee, Jesus calls some fishermen. They leave their fishing nets behind and follow Jesus at once.

If you would like to read the whole of this story, you will find it on page 66 of your Child's Bible.

Jesus wanders through Galilee. He teaches the people that God loves the innocent, the pure and the merciful.

If you would like to read the whole of this story,
you will find it on pages 71-73 of your Child's Bible.

A storm rages on the Sea of Galilee and the disciples are terrified. But Jesus sleeps peacefully. They wake him up and beg him to save them. He speaks to the waves: "Be calm." At once the wind drops and all is calm again. Jesus tells his disciples: "You must have more faith in me!"

If you would like to read the whole of this story, you will find it on page 74 of your Child's Bible.

There are just five loaves and two fishes for thousands of people! But Jesus works a great miracle, and all have plenty to eat!

If you would like to read the whole of this story,
you will find it on pages 74-75 of your Child's Bible.

Who will God decide is worthy of everlasting life – life that never ends? Jesus teaches us: "It is those who love God and their fellow men who will inherit my Kingdom!"

If you would like to read the whole of this story,
you will find it on pages 78-81 of your Child's Bible.

Jesus also tells us the story of the rich farmer, and warns us: "Don't store up earthly riches! You must become rich in the sight of God instead! You must store up treasure in Heaven – and that means you must care for others and share with those in need."

If you would like to read the whole of this story,
you will find it on pages 81-82 of your Child's Bible.

Jesus says: "I am the Good Shepherd! I know my sheep and they know me. If one of them strays, then I bring it back!"

If you would like to read the whole of this story,
you will find it on pages 82-83 of your Child's Bible.

"Father, I have sinned against God and against you. I don't deserve to be called your son any more!" But the father takes pity on his repentant child and says: "We must celebrate with a feast, because I am so happy that my son has come back to me to stay!"

If you would like to read the whole of this story, you will find it on pages 83-84 of your Child's Bible.

The blind man calls out: "Jesus, son of David, have pity on me!" Jesus turns to him and says: "I give you back your sight. Your faith has healed you!"

If you would like to read the whole of this story,
you will find it on pages 87-88 of your Child's Bible.

Jesus speaks to the rich tax collector, Zacchaeus: "Come down! Today I am going to stay in your house." The others are indignant. "He is going to stay at the house of a sinner!" they say. But Zacchaeus is converted. For Jesus seeks out the lost ones and wants to save them – even today.

If you would like to read the whole of this story,
you will find it on pages 88-89 of your Child's Bible.

Jesus washes his disciples' feet. Then he says to them:
"Just as I have washed your feet, so you too must serve
one another and wash each other's feet. You must love one
another!"

If you would like to read the whole of this story,
you will find it on pages 92-93 of your Child's Bible.

Jesus prays fervently to his Father in Heaven. In his great anguish he even sweats blood. He warns his disciples: "Watch and pray!"

If you would like to read the whole of this story,
you will find it on pages 93-94 of your Child's Bible.

Jesus dies on the Cross. No one can show greater love than to give his life for others. Jesus has given his life for us sinners. Thanks to him, we now have the possibility of getting to Heaven. Jesus loves us so much!

If you would like to read the whole of this story, you will find it on pages 98-99 of your Child's Bible.

The angel says to the women: "Don't be frightened! You are looking for Jesus of Nazareth, who died on the Cross. He is not here. He has risen!"

If you would like to read the whole of this story,
you will find it on pages 99-100 of your Child's Bible.

Jesus joins two disciples, who are going to Emmaus. But the disciples don't recognise him. Later they sit down to eat together. Jesus says the Blessing, breaks the Bread and gives it to them. At that moment he disappears.
The disciples' eyes are opened and they realise it was Jesus!

If you would like to read the whole of this story,
you will find it on pages 100-102 of your Child's Bible.

On Pentecost, Mary the Mother of God and the apostles of Jesus are gathered in prayer. The Holy Spirit comes down from Heaven in tongues of fire and the sound of a rushing wind. They are filled with the Holy Spirit. Now they have the courage to proclaim the words and deeds of Jesus fearlessly.

If you would like to read the whole of this story, you will find it on pages 104-105 of your Child's Bible.